UNICEF BOOK OF
CHILDREN'S SONGS

UNICEF
BOOK OF

Musical arrangements by
DENES AGAY

English lyrics by
JOAN GILBERT VAN POZNAK

CHILDREN'S SONGS

compiled and with
photographs by
William I. Kaufman

prepared for English-reading children by
ROSAMOND V. P. KAUFMAN
JOAN GILBERT VAN POZNAK

STACKPOLE BOOKS

B ecause the language of a child's heart is universal, the photographs and songs have been arranged to complement each other, according to the meaning and feeling of each, rather than by the country from which each comes.

UNICEF BOOK OF CHILDREN'S SONGS

Copyright © 1970 by William I. Kaufman

Published by
  STACKPOLE BOOKS
  Cameron and Kelker Streets, Harrisburg, Pa. 17105, U.S.A.

Library of Congress Catalog Card Number: 78-110478
ISBN 0-8117-1809-3
Printed in U.S.A.

Introduction

*M*usic is everywhere. If we listen. It is in the sounds of nature: the birds, the insects, the animals, the rustling of the leaves and the bubbling of the waters. We can hear music in the chores we do as we use our implements. If we listen, we can hear music as we walk along crowded city streets or solitary country roads. Everything has some harmony, dissonance, melody, or rhythm at the same time it has sound, and these sounds are regulated and arranged according to our ways of life.

This has always been true, and that is what makes this book of folk songs so interesting. The words and music have been shaped by the different ways of life, at different times in the history of the countries from which they come. Many of these folk songs have never been transcribed before, and most of them have never appeared in the English language.

In this collection there are songs about things in nature children especially love: the trees, the flowers, the speckled birds. There are songs about the barnyard creatures and songs about delicious things to eat: the guava berries, oranges, and olives. There are songs about playing instruments, celebrating birthdays, falling in love, being a naughty boy or a dancing maiden.

Some songs in this book make us laugh and some touch our hearts and make us feel quiet and thoughtful inside. All of them have come to us from the past, but they are very much a part of the lives of today's boys and girls who still sing them with pleasure. You will find lullabies and work songs and nonsense jingles in this book; and when you have learned these songs, I hope you come to know and understand that when we make music together, we are able to jump over the barriers of language and meet on the common ground of the most beautiful of all the sounds of life.

WILLIAM I. KAUFMAN

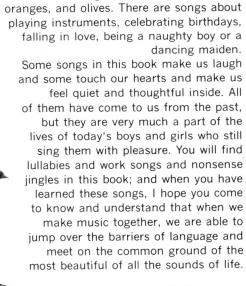

about the musical arrangements

Many of these songs, particularly those from Africa and Asia, originate in musical cultures far removed from Western traditions, especially from Western harmonic concepts. The indigenous musical instruments accompanying them also differ substantially from ours. Furthermore, on their home grounds some of these melodies are performed unaccompanied, perhaps only against the rhythmic background of a drum or hand clapping.

The piano arrangements we devised try to preserve and convey the native charm and originality of the songs. Chord symbols, provided for guitar or other suitable instruments, are only suggestions and are intended as an aid to help Western performances of these melodic gems.

DENES AGAY

Bubbles and Bubbles

Then I'll stitch a dress from a pass-ing cloud, Mount a bird and fly far a-bove the crowd. Un - cle Moon bathes his long white beard in milk, Come, I'll lull you to sleep on puffs of silk. Bub-bles and bub-bles all shin-ing and shim-mer-ing, String them in neck-lac-es reck-less-ly glim-mer-ing.

Repeat from 𝄋

11

Photo: Ghana

the Fishermen

s Song

China (Hunan)

Rather slow

The wa – ter in the riv – er Clear and long, Be – low the shal–low wa – ter Lies deep quick– sand. Broth – er has gone fish – ing Then let me cast the net. Pa – pa dear, hold the helm And I'll row, you row Hey ho! Let me row.

Hand-Shadow

As each verse is sung, a hand-shadow is made of the animal

Moderately

Indonesia

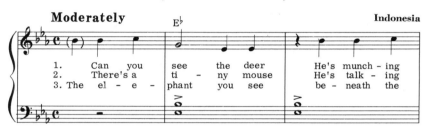

1. Can you see the deer He's munch - ing
2. There's a ti - ny mouse He's talk - ing
3. The el - e - phant you see be - neath the

leaves you hear: "Mil ke - te - mil mil ke - te -
to his spouse: "Tji tjit tju - wit tji tjit tju -
bam - boo tree "Nuk reng - gu - nuk nuk reng - gu -

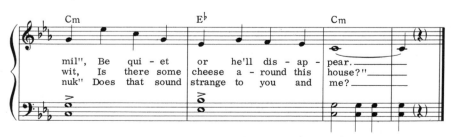

mil", Be qui - et or he'll dis - ap - pear.
wit, Is there some cheese a - round this house?"
nuk" Does that sound strange to you and me?

Photo: Kore

Song

ᖶhe BORDE

Moderately

Please let me pass, please let me pass. Where is the old, nar-row,

wind-ing lit-tle path? You are on it, this is the

nar-row toll path here. Please let me pass, oh won't you let me pass.

If you don't have a pass we can-not let you go.

We are on-ly go-ing to the shrine to play to-day,

18

R

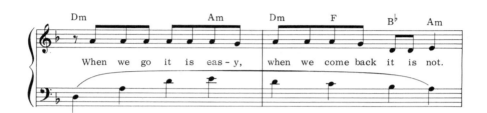

Photo: Indonesia

Photo: Colom

ARIRANG

Moderately

Korea

A - ri - rang,— A - ri - rang,— A - ra - ri - yo, A - ri - rang Val - ley,— how— well—— you grow. In our vil - lage the har - vest — is — good, All through the land — there — will — be plen - ty of food.

Photo: India

Suriram

Moderately

Malaysia

If it's pa - di*___ then say it's pa - di, Su - ri -
ram. So I don't have to toss___ and___ toss, Su - ri -
ram. And if you love me tell me that you
love___ me, Don't keep me wait - ing, I'm at a loss. Su - ri -

Chorus

ram ram ram___ Su - ri - ram, Su - ri - ram, oh, lis - ten to my

*padi is the rice grain with husk.

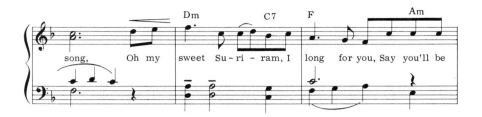

song, Oh my sweet Su-ri-ram, I long for you, Say you'll be

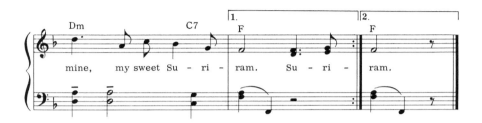

mine, my sweet Su - ri - ram. Su - ri - ram.

Photo: Indonesia

Dāphe

Nepal

Lively

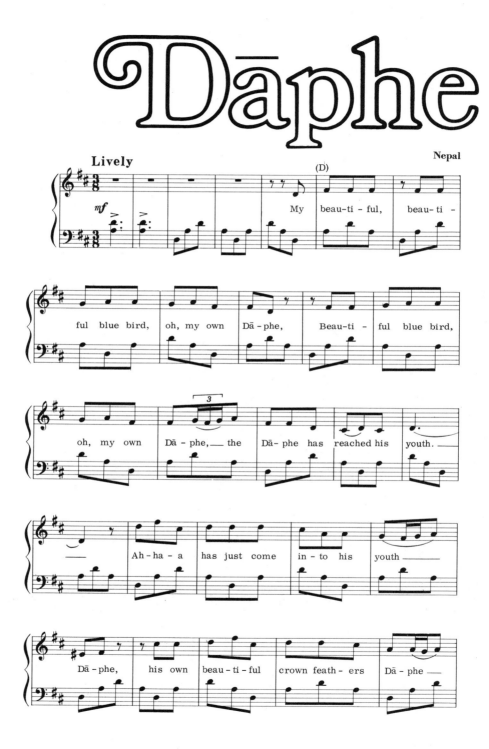

My beau-ti-ful, beau-ti-ful blue bird, oh, my own Dā-phe, Beau-ti-ful blue bird, oh, my own Dā-phe,— the Dā-phe has reached his youth.— Ah-ha-a has just come in-to his youth Dā-phe, his own beau-ti-ful crown feath-ers Dā-phe——

Bird

Photo: Korea

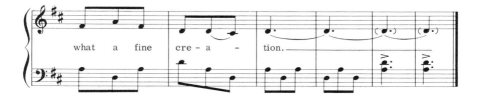

what a fine cre-a - tion.

lAd
TO pROVE his LOVE

Moderately lively

Philippines(Tagalog)

A lad to prove his love Up a tall pa - pa - ya
tree Climbed with a bas - ket full Of the
love he held for me. The top - most branch he
reached, It broke off with a click, Oh
my, what aw - ful luck, I'll need a new love quick!!

Photo: Ecuador

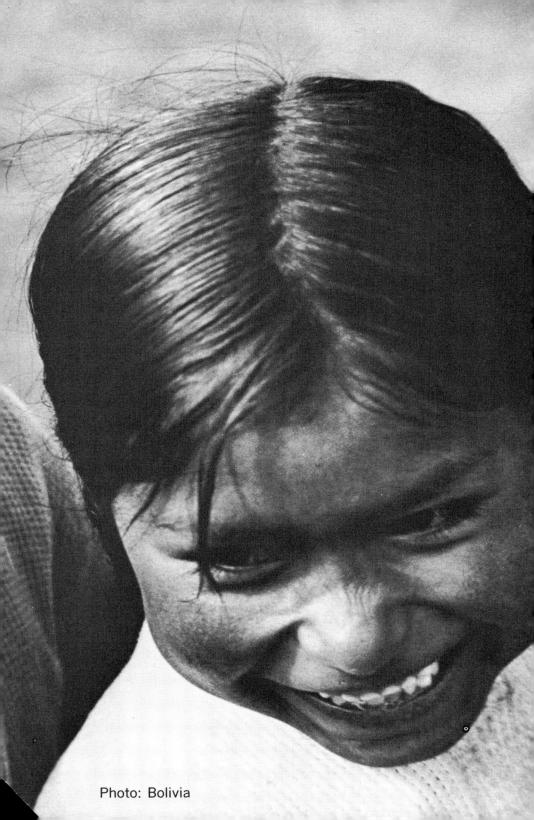

Photo: Bolivia

the New Dress

Moderately

Singapore (Chinese)

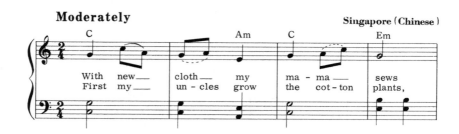

With new— cloth— my ma - ma — sews
First my— un - cles grow the cot - ton plants,

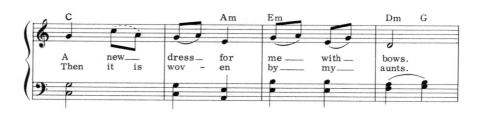

A new— dress— for me — with— bows.
Then it is wov - en by— my— aunts.

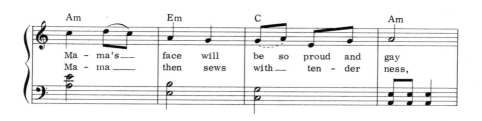

Ma - ma's— face will be so proud and gay
Ma - ma — then sews with— ten - der ness,

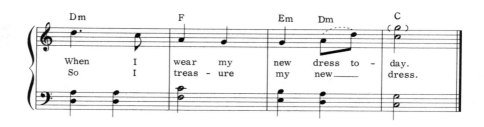

When I wear my new dress to - day.
So I treas - ure my new— dress.

Photo:

TWILIG

Moderately

Thailand

Birds fly____ back to their nests at twi-light time. Birds fly____ back to their____ nests at twi-light time. I can hear the bam-boo pipes play - ing far a - way. Lan Taa___ Lan Ta___ Lan - Ta - lan - ta. Let us dance___ in the o - pen

34

HT

Photo: Thailand

air,　the　o - pen　air,　Let　us＿＿　dance＿＿ and＿＿

play　For it＿＿　is＿ the＿ end　of　day.＿＿

The Cock

Crows

Happily

Cameroon

The cock crows as the new day starts And all a - rise with
hap - py hearts. Ev - 'ry - one greets his ser - e - nade,
Now all the good cous - cous* is made. Pi - lon pon pon, Pi -
lon pon pon, pi - lon pon pon, The day's be - gun.

*Couscous.. North African culinary specialty, the origins of which date back to earliest times.
Couscous is made with millet flour or with crushed rice, and with meat.

the WHISTLE of the TRAIN

Lively   Congo

Pio, Pio, Pio,   Pio, Pio, Pio

The whis-tle of the train is go-ing Pio, Pio, Pio, It's

com-ing round the bend and blow-ing Pio, Pio, Pio.

D.S. 𝄋 ad lib.

Repeat song several times at different speeds. End it by singing it faster and faster, gradually fading out.

Photo: Cameroo

A

bena

Ghana

Moderately

A - be-na do you hear what I hear far a - way? Hear the drums go: kren kren ka, kren kren ka, kren - kren. Hear them cry - ing: yaa yaa su, yaa yaa su, yaa yaa. Hear the guns go: pom pom to, pom pom to, pom pom. A - be-na do you hear what I hear far a - way?

oto: Cameroon

The Fam

ine

Kenya (Akamba)

Moderately

1. Lis-ten now while I tell the sto - ry That is

well known in Ki - kam - ba Of the fam - ine in the—

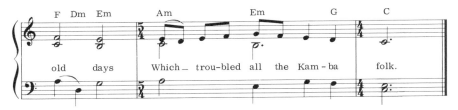

old days Which— trou-bled all the Kam - ba folk.

2. It is true what I have to tell you
Like the famine of the flour,
We were all as thin as wasps then,
Many of the Kamba people died.

3. After harvesting crops aplenty
From our farms this bounteous season
Put it all in granaries safely
And forget the hungering for wealth.

Photo: Korea

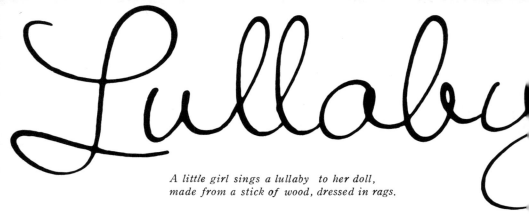

Lullaby

A little girl sings a lullaby to her doll,
made from a stick of wood, dressed in rags.

Senegal

Gently moving

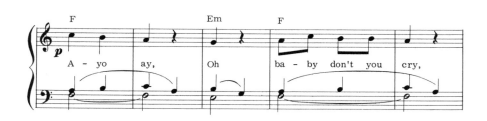

A - yo ay, Oh ba - by don't you cry,

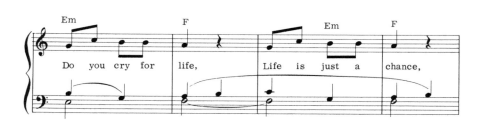

Do you cry for life, Life is just a chance,

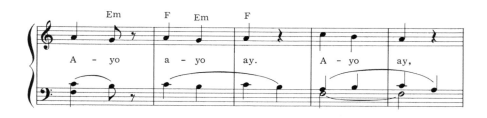

A - yo a - yo ay. A - yo ay,

Dipidu

Rather slowly

Uganda

mf Good day, Good day to you, Good day, O dip-i-du,

Good day, Good day to you, Good day, O dip-i-du.

Dip, dip, dip-i-du, Dip-i-du, O dip-i-du.

clap hands to the rhythm of the left hand

Dip dip dip dip dip-i-du, Dip-i-du, O dip-i-du.

Photo: Taiw

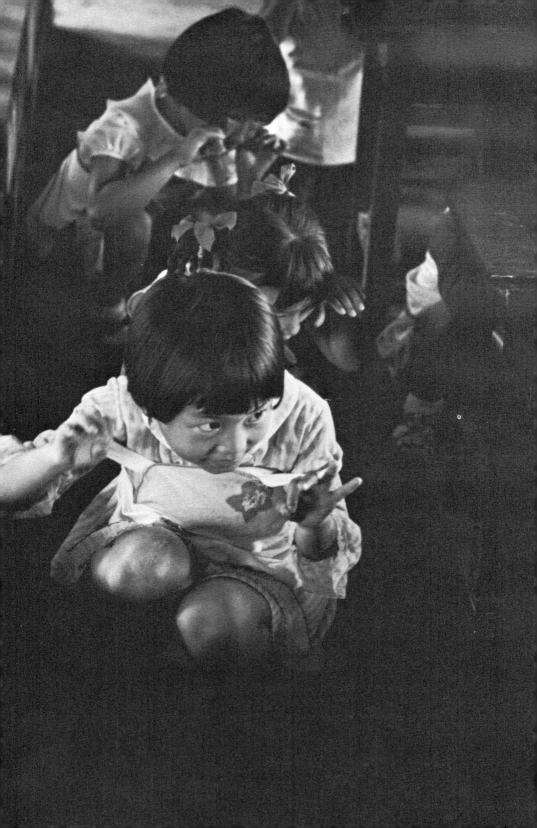

chick, chick little chickies

Gaily moving

stacc. sempre

Iran

Chick, chick lit-tle chick-ies, All my pret-ty lit-tle chick-ies,

Pret-ti-er than blos-soms peep-ing, All my lit-tle chicks are sleep-ing.

Soft and gen-tle___ they rest In their warm

lit-tle nests, I will com-fort___ them all;

they're so sweet and so small. Gold-en

48

as the sun is, Fluf - fy, ev - 'ry one is,

Oh what won - der-ful fun is, Just like

sug - ar___ spun is ev - 'ry pret - ty lit - tle chick - ie.

Chick, chick lit - tle chick - ies, All my pret - ty

lit - tle chick - ies, Pret - ti - er than blos - soms peep - ing

All my lit - tle chicks are sleep - ing, chick, chick.

49

HOW GOOD and JOYOUS

Round

Israel

[1] Dm / Gm / Dm / Gm

How good and joy-ous it is for broth-ers to

Dm A7 Dm / [2] Dm / / Gm

dwell to-geth-er. Good and joy-

Dm / Gm / Dm A7 Dm

ous for broth-ers to dwell to-geth-er.

Photo: Cameroon

Moderately

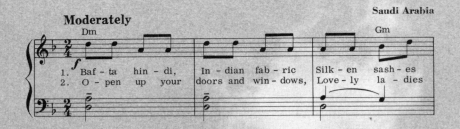

Dm / Gm

1. Baf - ta hin - di, In - dian fab - ric Silk - en sash - es
2. O - pen up your doors and win - dows, Love - ly la - dies

A / Dm / C / G / Gm

and cash - mere, Pret - ty things for pret - ty lass - es,
hear my cry, I have taf - fe - tas and em - broi-der-ies

Bafta Hindi

The Peddler

52

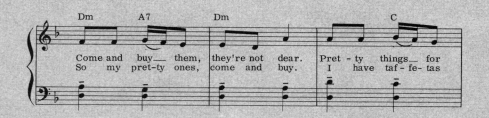

Come and buy them, they're not dear. Pret-ty things for
So my pret-ty ones, come and buy. I have taf-fe-tas

pret - ty lass - es, Come and buy them, they're not dear.
and em-broi-der-ies So my pret-ty ones, come and buy.

Photo: Tunisia

Oh, He Planted Ginger

Moderately lively

Bulgaria

1. Oh, he plant - ed gin - ger, Gin - ger grows so swift - ly,
2. So he fetched a bad wolf, To eat lit - tle goat up,

Then he fetched a lit - tle goat To graze on the gin - ger.
So he fetched a bad wolf To eat lit - tle goat up.

(1.) Lit - tle goat won't graze on gin - ger, Gin-ger grows so swift - ly.

(2.) Bad wolf won't eat lit - le goat up, Gin-ger grows so swift - ly.
Lit - tle goat won't graze on gin ger,

D.C. with
2nd verse

54

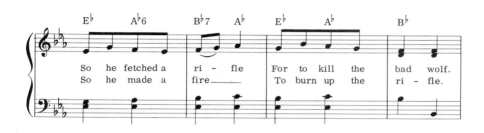

gradually faster

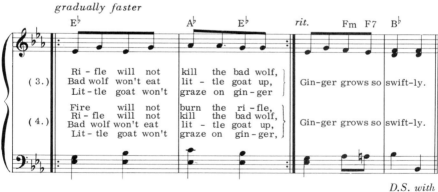

D.S. with
4th verse

Coda **Fast**

Sponge Fish

Moderately

Greece

Lit - tle ship we'll go — a — fish - ing Out in the sea, out in the sea. When the eve - ning bells — are — ring - ing Man - y spong - es we'll — be — bring - ing And we'll sail for land, — all — sing - ing Home from the sea, —————— Home from — the — sea.

Melody in lower voice

Photo: Ceylon

ing

Bill

Photo: Greece

y Goat

Moderately

Norway

1. Bil - ly, Bil - ly goat, my joy,
2. Your poor moth - er, I've heard tell,

Think u - pon your— lit - tle boy;
Came home late with— tin - kling bell;

Bru - in may with
And out sprang that

hug so tight Cap - ture you this— ver - y night.
dread - ful bear, Ate her up as — she stood there.

3. You're so small, I am afraid
Bruin's supper you have made.
Billy! that would be too bad –
For you're such a clever lad!

4. Billy, Billy answer, do!
Come to those who wait for you!
Not yet please, O goat, my joy,
Can you leave your little boy!

Andantino

Turkey

Pret - ty ba - by, Your __ cra - dle

sleep well, be __ still __ I will rock you to __ sleep, __ yes I will __
is hewn of __ pine, __ I will rock you be there rain __ or __ shine, __

As __ stead-y as __ wa-ter turns the mill. __ Nen ni __ nen ni __
For your heart is as __ one with __ mine. __

Nen ni __ nen ni __ Nen ni __ nen ni __ Nen ni Ba - by

mine. Ba-by mine.

60

Mine

Photo: Bolivia

Butterfly

Moderately

Yugoslavia (Serbia)

Child: Lit - tle but - ter - fly, my friend, will you come here a min - ute? Look I have a love - ly rose, why don't you smell what's in it?

Butterfly: I would come ex - cept that nee - dles fill me with a hor - ror. First you'll pinch me, then you'll prick me, then there's no to - mor - row.

Look I have a love - ly rose, why then you'll prick me,

don't you smell what's in it? then there's no to - mor - row.

Child: No I won't, my butterfly, I cross my heart and promise,
I just want to count how many wee legs you have, honest.

Butterfly: I can tell you this, my boy, but only at a distance,
Butterflies have got six legs-now I'll be off. . good riddance!

Photo: Jap

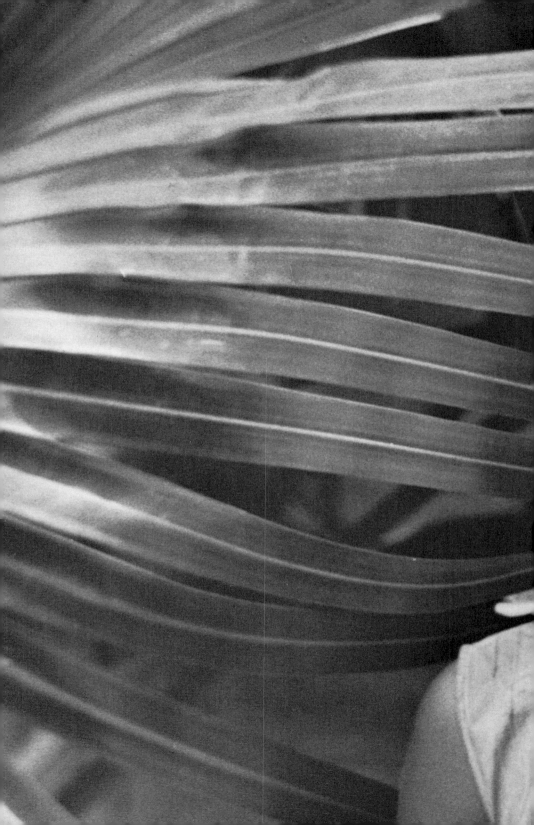

Photo: India

La Imilla

Moderately fast

Bolivia

Dance your dance,— I-mi - lla,

Lit -tle face — dark as clay, With the grace — of a reed

In the breeze — as you sway. Whirl-ing skirt the mer - ry

col - or of a cher - ry And your bright — yel-low sash,

Like the sun's — shin -ing flash. flash.

Repeat from sign (𝄋)

Photo: Thailar

Samba-le-le

Lively

Brazil

Sam-ba-le-le he is cra - zy, It's ver-y hard to en-dure him.

Sam-ba - le-le if he stays, he Needs eight -een slaps they may

cure him. Sam - ba! Sam - ba! Sam-ba - le - le,

Lift up your skirt and then run on your way. Sam-ba! Sam-ba!

Sam-ba - le-le, Step on the ruf-fle and shuf-fle a - way!

BEAUTIFUL

Tenderly

Chile

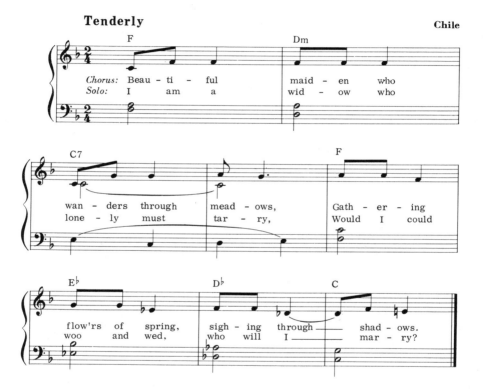

Chorus: Beau - ti - ful maid - en who wan - ders through mead - ows, Gath - er - ing flow'rs of spring, sigh - ing through shad - ows.

Solo: I am a wid - ow who lone - ly must tar - ry, Would I could woo and wed, who will I mar - ry?

Chorus: Beautiful maiden, why
keep on refusing,
Here are one hundred
young men for your choosing.

Solo: I choose Antonio;
he'll be true to me,
His eyes dance, and his glance
never looks gloomy.

Chorus: Now that you found your true
beloved treasure,
Side by side, groom and bride
long live in pleasure.

70

Photo: Indi

MAIDEN

YESTERDAY MORNING

Very lively

Colombia

1. Oh yes - ter - day at morn - ing And then to - day at dawn, Oh yes - ter - day at morn - ing and then to - day at dawn, The tur - tle - doves were sing - ing, The roost - ers sang a - long", Ki - ki - ri, ki - ki - ri, I'm hap - py as can

2. (The) par - rot was pro - claim - ing be - fore the cen - ti - pede, The par - rot was pro - claim - ing be - fore the cen - ti - pede, The old bird kept in - sist - ing, "The truth is what we need",

Refrain

be;   Ki - ki - ri,   ki - ki - - ri,   But

who a - wak - en'd me?_____   2. 3. The   me.
4. A

3. The dogs for miles and miles
   Were barking at the moon, *(repeat)*
   A silly goose was cackling
   And thought she sang a tune.
   Ki-ki-ri, etc.

4. A heavy rain was falling
   And when it rains it pours, *(repeat)*
   With thunder, wind and lightning,
   I wish I had some oars.
   Ki-ki-ri, etc.

Photo: Sierra Leone

Anton

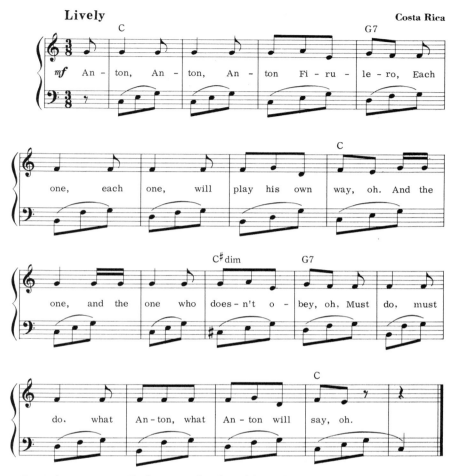

Lively

Costa Rica

An - ton, An - ton, An - ton Fi - ru - le - ro, Each one, each one, will play his own way, oh. And the one, and the one who does - n't o - bey, oh, Must do, must do, what An - ton, what An - ton will say, oh.

The children sit in a row. The director stands in front of them and indicates what instrument each child is to imitate.

They clap hands rythmically during the song, excepting the moment in which each player imitates the instrument which the director indicates with his hands.

The imaginary instruments are the following: flutes, clarinets, trumpets, pianos, accordions, etc.

Whoever comes in late on the imitation must take consequences.

Firulero

THE
SPECKLED BIRD

Lively

G   Ecuador

The grey speck-led bird-ie was play - ing

As she sat in the green lem - on tree,

With her beak she broke off some small branch - es,

Then a flow - er she plucked from a - bove.

Ay, ay, ay, you are my love.

Matatero - terola

Guatemala

Moderately

1. A good morn-ing to you, my mas-ter, Ma - ta - te - ro-te-ro-
2. And what job shall we of - fer to her,

la. Will you give me one of your daugh-ters, Ma - ta -
Let's make Mar - ti - ta the dish - wash - er,

te – ro – te – ro – la. Which of all of them would most
It's a job that's not to her

please you, Ma – ta – te – ro – te – ro – la, Most of
lik – ing, Then let's

all I pre – fer Mar – ti – ta, Ma – ta – te – ro – te – ro – la.
make her the prin – ce's daugh – ter,

D.C. with 2nd verse

Photo: Afghanistan

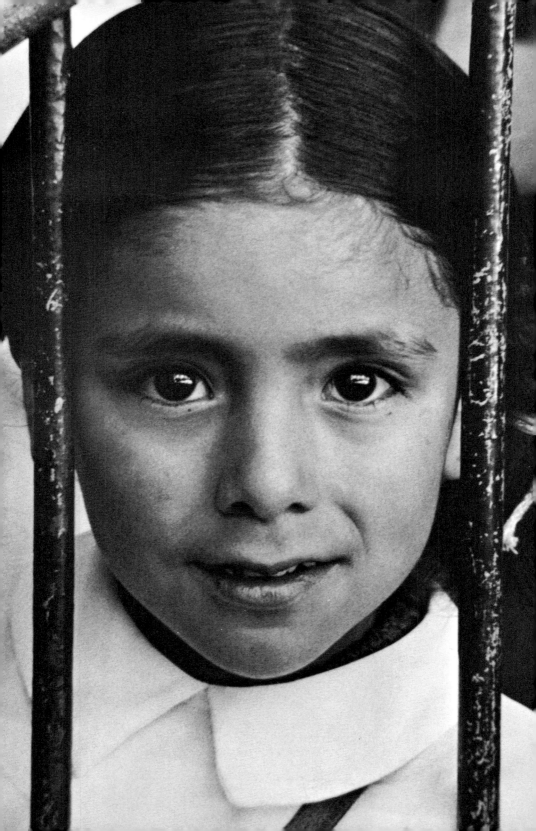

Oranges Sweet

Moderately lively

Mexico

Or-an-ges sweet and some lem-on sli-ces, Give me a hug for your eye en-

ti - ces. If all my prom - is - es in De - cem - ber Are false, by

May you will not re - mem - ber. The march is play - ing, my heart is

griev - ing, Good-bye now, Mad - ame, for I am leav - ing. To my wee

house I will go a - lone, I'll buy some ta - cos and give you none.

Photo: Bolivia

Photo: Uganda

The River

Moderately   Cm   E♭+   **Peru**

1. From the reed a lit – tle flow – er Fell in –
2. Then a flute that was a shep – herd's Fell in –

E♭   Cm6   A♭

to the riv – er, oh, And it made the riv – er
to the riv – er, oh, And it made the riv – er

Cm   Cm6   G7   Cm

hap – py As its per – fume joined the flow.
hap – py As its mu – sic joined the flow. *(hum)*

A♭   E♭   Cm   F9   G7   Cm

3. Silent tear drops of a maiden
   Fell into the river, oh,
   And it made the river happy;
   Crystal clear became its flow.

4. As the shepherd's flute, the tear drops
   And the flower joined the flow,
   They all made the river happy;
   So it never let them go.

Photo: Sierra Leon

Lively

Venezuela

Let's go to the or - chard of Ton - to - ral - lere To vis - it Do - na - na who's pick - ing ap - ples there. Do - na - na is - n't here, she's in her flow - er bed; She's o - pen - ing ro - ses and paint - ing them red.

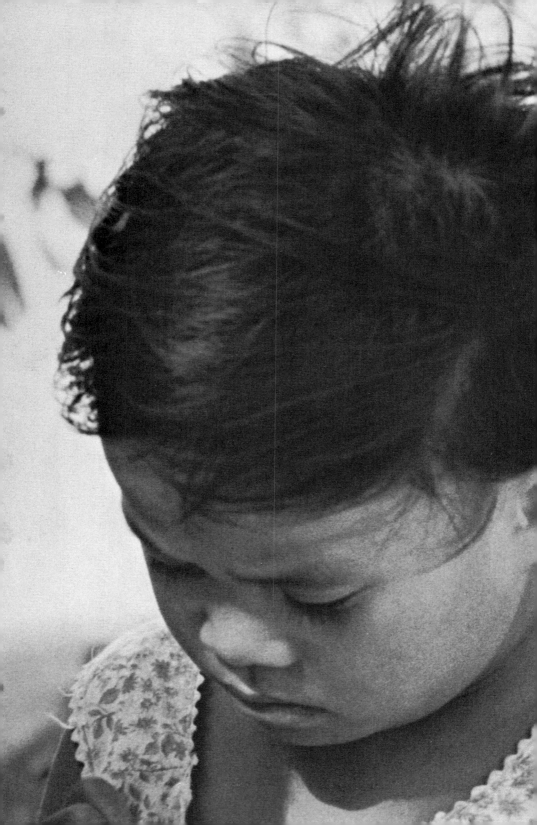

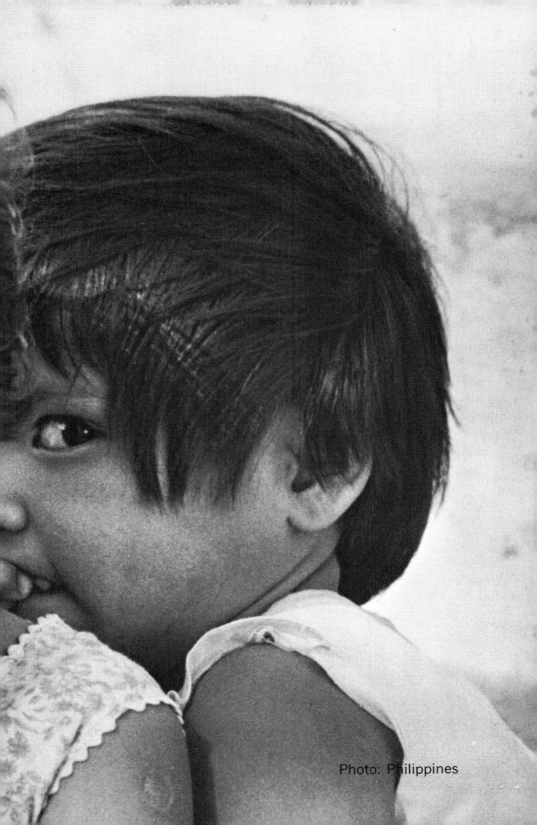

Photo: Philippines

Guava Berry Song

A Christmas Song

St. John,
U.S. Virgin Islands

Moderately lively

Come let us be joy-ful, and min-gle our song And hail the sweet joys which this day brings a-long. We join our glad voic-es in one hymn of praise To Him who has kept us, and length-ened our days. A mer-ry Christ-mas to you all, A mer-ry

Christ - mas to you all, A mer - ry Christ-mas, A mer - ry

Christ - mas, A mer - ry Christ - mas to you all!

Bright Calypso rhythm

Good morn - in', good morn - in', We wish you a mer-ry Christ-mas, Good

morn - in', good morn - in', We wish you a mer - ry Christ-mas, Good

morn - in', good morn - in', We've come for the gua - va ber - ry, Good

morn - in', good morn - in', Oh put it on the ta - ble.

Photo: Sierra Leone

Acknowledgment

I am indebted to so many for their help and coopera-
tion that it would take a world almanac to include
everyone by name who has made this vast project
possible. To UNICEF in New York, Paris, and in each
of the forty-two countries I visited I am especially
grateful. Special thanks to Terence R. Bech, who
collected, transcribed and translated *The Dāphe Bird*
song from Nepal. To the ambassadors, ministers of
education, ministers of culture and information,
consular staffs and members of the staffs of the
permanent missions to the United Nations, UNESCO
staffs, religious leaders, translators, scholars, individual
researchers, writers, parents and staffs of various
welfare agencies for children who helped in the collect-
ing of the written material, I say, "Bless you and
thanks." I dream that all our efforts will help all
our children to a greater understanding of each other.

WILLIAM I. KAUFMAN

about
William I. Kaufman

WILLIAM I. KAUFMAN's love of children and belief that
they are the hope of the world have led him to take on
the almost impossible task of compiling material and
photographing for this volume in forty-two countries.
His over eighty books on a variety of subjects are published in English, French, German, Italian, Swedish,
Japanese, Danish, Spanish and Arabic. Starting in the
theater and continuing in television, he has pursued a
successful creative life as a communications executive
and consultant, a theatrical producer, a writer-editor,
a teacher, a photographer and a song writer.

Design by Krone Art Service